W9-AWU-219

Contents

© Creative Publications 32301

Introduction

Mastering subtraction facts provides children with basic tools that will help them achieve success in mathematics. This book provides efficient, motivating practice for memorizing those facts.

Overview

The prerequisites pages pinpoint key understandings that create a foundation upon which children can successfully learn basic facts. Use the information provided there to evaluate your children's readiness for the activities in this book. These pages also offer some simple activities to develop readiness and list resources that contain additional activities to use with children who need further preparation.

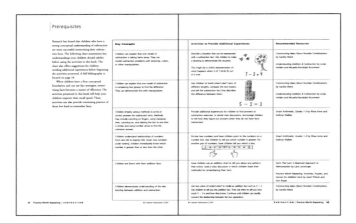

The strategy summary pages list strategies children often use to learn their subtraction facts. Abbreviated information about each strategy is included.

> **notes** A subtraction fact test is provided on pages 2–4 of this book. Use this test to identify the specific subtraction facts each student needs to practice.

© Creative Publications 32301

Practice Worth Repeating

**Activities, Puzzles, and Games
for Subtraction Facts**

Janet Pittock

Creative Publications

Acknowledgments

Writer Janet Pittock

Editor Diane Nieker

Design Director Karen Lee

Design Gerta Sorensen

Cover Illustration Amanda Haley

Illustrators Sarah Frederking, Tammie Lyon

Production Carlisle Communications, Ltd.

©1999 Creative Publications®, Inc.

Two Prudential Plaza

Chicago, IL 60601

Creative Publications is a registered trademark.

Printed in the United States of America.

All rights reserved.

Unless otherwise stated on selected pages in this book,
no part of this publication may be reproduced, or
copied into or stored in a retrieval system, or trans-
mitted, in any form or by any means, electronic,
mechanical, photocopying, recording, or otherwise,
without the prior written permission of the publisher.

ISBN: 0-7622-1202-0

Catalog No. 32301

Customer Service 800-624-0822

http://www.creativepublications.com

2 3 4 5 6 7 8 ML 05 04 03 02 01 00

●
**Whole Class
Activity**

●●●

**Small Group
Activity**

●

**Individual
Practice
Activity**

The activities in this book will help children focus on and improve their fact recall. These activities can be used over and over again, even with the same students.

There are three types of activities:

▶ Activities led by the teacher

▶ Games for two to four children

▶ Activities in which children focus on specific sets of facts they need to practice. Many of the individual practice activities can be used as homework.

Throughout this book you will find that the term *minuend* is used to describe the number from which an amount is being subtracted and the term *subtrahend* is used to describe the amount being subtracted. The answer to a subtraction fact will be referred to as the *difference*.

$$
\begin{array}{r}
15 \quad \text{minuend} \\
-\ 7 \quad \text{subtrahend} \\
\hline
8 \quad \text{difference}
\end{array}
$$

© Creative Publications 32301

Prerequisites

Research has found that children who have a strong conceptual understanding of subtraction are more successful memorizing their subtraction facts. The following chart summarizes key understandings your children should exhibit before using the activities in this book. The chart also offers suggestions for children needing additional experiences before beginning the activities presented. A full bibliography is located on page 24.

When children have a firm conceptual foundation and can use fact strategies, memorizing facts becomes a matter of efficiency. The activities presented in this book will help your children improve their recall speed. These activities can also provide continuing practice of those few hard-to-remember facts.

Key Concepts

Children can explain that one model of subtraction is taking items away. They can model subtraction problems with drawings, cubes, or other manipulatives.

Children can explain that one model of subtraction is comparing two groups to find the difference. They can demonstrate this with manipulatives.

Children employ various methods to arrive at correct answers for subtraction facts. Methods may include counting on fingers, using manipulatives, counting up, and relating the fact to one that is similar and using number sense to find the unknown answer.

Children understand relationships of numbers from zero (0) to twenty (20). Given two numbers under twenty, children immediately know which number is greater than or less than the other.

Children are fluent with their addition facts.

Children demonstrate understanding of the relationship between addition and subtraction.

© Creative Publications 32301

Activities to Provide Additional Experiences	Recommended Resources
Describe a situation that can be represented with a subtraction fact. Ask children to make a drawing to demonstrate the situation. This might be a child's representation of what happens when 3 of 7 birds fly out of a tree. $7 - 3 = 4$	*Constructing Ideas About Number Combinations* by Sandra Ward. *Understanding Addition & Subtraction* by Linda Holden and Micaelia Randolph Brummett.
Ask children to build LinkerCube® towers of different lengths, compare the two towers, and tell the subtraction fact that describes the difference between them. $5 - 2 = 3$	*Constructing Ideas About Number Combinations* by Sandra Ward. *Understanding Addition & Subtraction* by Linda Holden and Micaelia Randolph Brummett.
Provide additional experiences for children to find answers to subtraction exercises. In whole class discussions, encourage children to tell how they figure out answers when they do not have facts memorized.	*Smart Arithmetic, Grades 1-3* by Rhea Irvine and Kathryn Walker.
Dictate two numbers and have children point to the numbers on a number line. Ask children to tell you which number is greater. For another pair of numbers, have children tell you which is less.	*Smart Arithmetic, Grades 1–3* by Rhea Irvine and Kathryn Walker.
Have children use an addition chart to tell you about any patterns they notice. Lead a class discussion in which children share their method(s) for remembering their facts.	*Facts That Last: A Balanced Approach to Memorization* by Larry Leutzinger. *Practice Worth Repeating: Activities, Puzzles, and Games for Addition Facts* by Janet Pittock and Ann Roper.
Use two colors of LinkerCubes® to model an addition fact such as 3 + 2. Ask children to tell you the addition fact. Then ask them to tell you how much 5 − 3 is and how they know. Continue until children can readily connect the relationship between the two operations.	*Constructing Ideas About Number Combinations* by Sandra Ward.

Fact Strategies Summary

Children often struggle to remember certain groups of facts. Help make the task of committing those facts to memory easier for your children. First, identify which facts each child needs to spend more time working on. Then, review strategies designed to help children learn those facts. A summary of the strategies follows.

Count-back Strategy

When subtracting 0, 1, 2, or 3, count back from the minuend. For example, with $12 - 3$, start from 12 and count back three numbers, 11, 10, 9. Thus $12 - 3 = 9$. This strategy works best when subtracting 0, 1, 2, or 3.

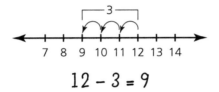

$$12 - 3 = 9$$

Count-up Strategy

When subtracting two numbers that are close together, count up from the lower number. For example, with $11 - 8 = \square$, start with 8 and count up 9, 10, 11. Three numbers are counted up, so $11 - 8 = 3$.

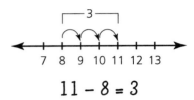

$$11 - 8 = 3$$

Fact-Families Strategy

Fact families are groups of two or four related addition and subtraction facts. The fact-families strategy can be used with all subtraction facts.

$$3 - 2 = 1 \qquad 2 + 1 = 3$$
$$3 - 1 = 2 \qquad 1 + 2 = 3$$

© Creative Publications 32301

Think-Addition Strategy

To find the difference for a subtraction fact, think of the related addition fact. Since $3 + 5 = 8$, $8 - 3 = 5$. The think-addition strategy can be used with any subtraction fact.

$$8 - 3 = \square \quad \rightarrow \quad \square + 3 = 8$$

Patterns Strategy

Some facts become easy to remember because they follow a pattern. For example, any number minus itself is always equal to zero. The easiest patterns are for subtracting 0, 1, 10, 9, subtracting the minuend from itself, and subtracting one less than the minuend.

$$5 - 4 = 1$$
$$4 - 3 = 1$$
$$3 - 2 = 1$$

Subtract-from-Ten Strategy

This strategy involves visualizing the removal of counters from a ten-frame. Use this strategy when subtracting from ten.

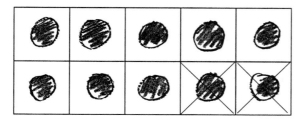

$$10 - 2 = 8$$

Ten-Between Strategy

When the number ten lies between the two numbers of the subtraction fact, find the distance from ten for each of the numbers, then add their distances together.

The ten-between strategy is easiest to use when neither minuend nor subtrahend is far from ten.

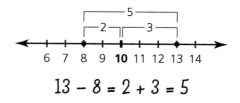

$$13 - 8 = 2 + 3 = 5$$

Activity 1 | Finding Your Facts

● **Whole Class Activity**

Description

Three 20- to 30-minute fact tests identify which subtraction facts each child has difficulty recalling. When choosing facts to practice in subsequent activities, children should focus on the ones they were not able to recall easily.

Materials

▶ Subtraction Chart, page 5, one (1) per child

▶ Fact Test, page 4, three (3) copies per child, plus (3) copies for use as a test key

▶ One (1) set of subtraction flash cards to include differences 0 through 10, separated into three sets

Time

Each test takes twenty (20) to thirty (30) minutes. You may want to spread the tests over a three-day period.

Five minutes per child interview.

> **notes** Allow children only as much time as it takes for you to write down the entire fact and answer. This will help to ascertain whether or not children have quick recall of facts.

Giving the Tests

❶ Give each child a copy of the fact test.

❷ Choose one of the three sets of flash cards. Show a fact to the class and read the fact aloud.

❸ Record each fact, including the answer, after the corresponding number on your paper after you read the fact to the class. Children should write only the answer. Your copy of the fact test will serve as your answer key.

❹ Show, say, and record the next fact. Follow this procedure through the set of flash cards.

❺ Repeat this process for the other two sets of flash cards.

© Creative Publications 32301

Correcting the Tests

1 Use the answer keys you created during each test. Write the complete fact (2 + 3 = 5) after each incorrect answer on the children's papers.

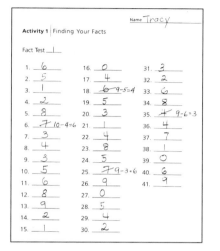

Name Tracy

Activity 1 | Finding Your Facts

Fact Test __1__

1. 6	16. 0	31. 3
2. 5	17. 4	32. 2
3. 1	18. 6 9-5=4	33. 6
4. 2	19. 5	34. 8
5. 8	20. 3	35. 4 9-6=3
6. 7 10-4=6	21. 1	36. 4
7. 3	22. 4	37. 7
8. 4	23. 8	38. 1
9. 3	24. 5	39. 0
10. 5	25. 7 9-3=6	40. 6
11. 6	26. 9	41. 9
12. 8	27. 0	
13. 9	28. 5	
14. 2	29. 4	
15. 1	30. 2	

2 Prepare a subtraction chart for each child on which all facts the child missed are highlighted. As you do this, keep track of the most frequently missed facts so you can focus on them during whole class activities.

3 After all three tests have been administered, checked, and individual subtraction charts have been prepared, meet with each child individually to discuss results.

4 Children who have many facts to practice may need to gain more experience, or they may need additional practice in using fact strategies. For more information, see pages iv through 1.

notes A special subtraction chart has been created for this book. You'll find a reproducible version of this chart on page 5. The minuends are along the left, the subtrahends along the right. To find a difference, read down the diagonal column from the subtrahend until you reach the number in the row of the minuend. The simplified chart below highlights the fact 5 − 3 = 2.

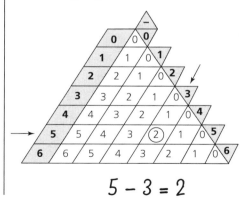

$$5 - 3 = 2$$

Activity 1 Finding Your Facts

Fact Test _____

1. _____	16. _____	31. _____
2. _____	17. _____	32. _____
3. _____	18. _____	33. _____
4. _____	19. _____	34. _____
5. _____	20. _____	35. _____
6. _____	21. _____	36. _____
7. _____	22. _____	37. _____
8. _____	23. _____	38. _____
9. _____	24. _____	39. _____
10. _____	25. _____	40. _____
11. _____	26. _____	41. _____
12. _____	27. _____	
13. _____	28. _____	
14. _____	29. _____	
15. _____	30. _____	

 © Creative Publications 32301

Activity 1 | Finding Your Facts

One (1) copy per child plus one (1) copy for the teacher.

Subtraction Chart

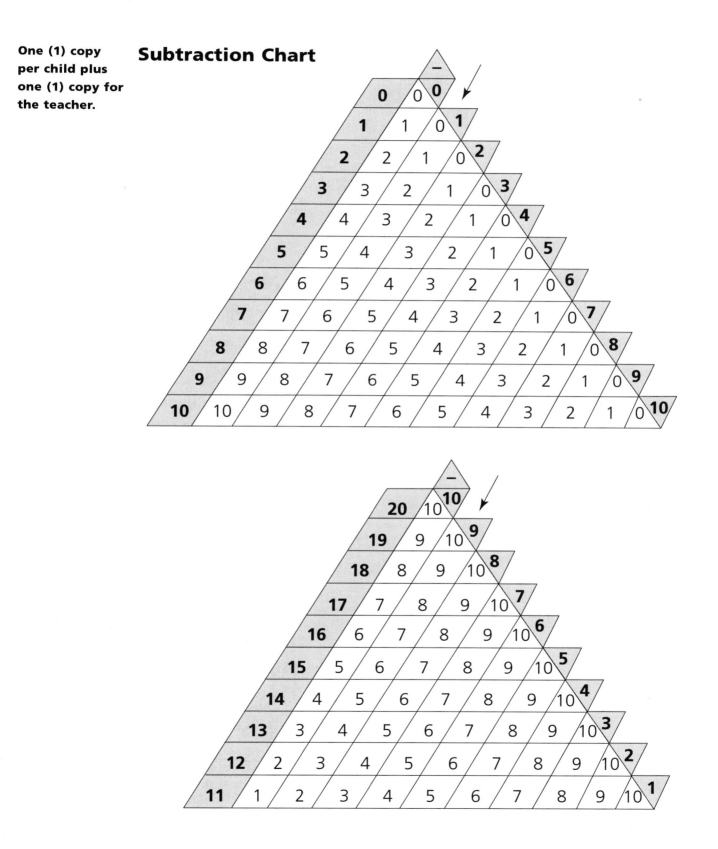

Activity 2 | Subtraction Pop-up

Whole Class Activity

Description
In Subtraction Pop-up, each student is assigned a number between 0 and 10. As you say each subtraction fact, children assigned the number that represents the difference stand up.

Materials
Subtraction flash cards

Time
5 to 15 minutes

Getting Ready to Play
Assign each child a number between 0 and 10.

> **notes** Make this practice effective by focusing on facts you have determined many children in the class still need to memorize. Also, try to assign differences to children that correspond to facts they still need to memorize.

Playing the Game

❶ Show and read a flash card. As you say each fact, children assigned the number that represents the difference should stand up.

❷ Have the children sit down as the whole class says the entire fact out loud.

❸ Repeat. Keep track of the facts as you go so that you can vary the groups of children who stand up.

❹ Vary the game
  a. Award a point to the first child that stands up in response to each fact.
  b. Assign each child two differences.
  c. Give children a subtraction fact rather than just a number. Have them stand up when that fact or when a fact with the same difference is given.
  d. Allow the child who stands up first for a fact to give the next fact.

© Creative Publications 32301

Activity 3 | Subtract-tac-toe

Whole Class Activity

Description

This version of tic-tac-toe gets children thinking about which subtraction facts produce specific differences.

Materials

None

Time

Three (3) minutes per game. Repeat as desired.

Getting Ready to Play

❶ Draw a tic-tac-toe grid on the board and write the numerals 1 through 9 in the spaces.

1	2	3
4	5	6
7	8	9

❷ Divide the class into two teams, A and B.

Playing the Game

❶ The object of the game is to capture three spaces in a row vertically, horizontally, or diagonally.

❷ Ask a member of Team A to select the number in the grid they want to capture and give a subtraction fact with a difference equal to that number. If they give a correct fact, mark their space with an "X." If they give an incorrect fact, no space is marked.

❸ Ask Team B to select a number and give their subtraction fact. If correct, mark their space with an "O."

❹ Continue until one team wins or the game is a draw.

❺ Repeat as desired.

Activity 4 | Cross off

●●●
**Small Group
Activity**

**One (1) copy
per group.
Also see
page 9.**

Description

Add the numbers rolled on two number cubes and use the sum as a number in a subtraction fact. Cross the number off of your number list. The first one to cross all of the numbers off of his or her list wins!

Materials

▶ Subtraction chart, page 5

▶ A pair of number cubes

▶ A copy of Cross off, page 9, for each player

Time

About 15 minutes

Playing the Game

1 Take turns rolling the number cubes. Add the numbers rolled, then write a subtraction fact and its difference using that sum as one of the numbers. Use only facts that can be found on the subtraction chart.

2 Write your fact and difference on the game page. Then cross the numbers used off your list. (Sometimes you might write a fact that gives you no new numbers to cross off.)

3 Continue playing until one player crosses all of the numbers off his or her list.

© Creative Publications 32301

Activity 4 | Cross off

One (1) copy
per player.

Write each subtraction fact and difference below. Be sure to cross
the numbers you used off your number list.

Number List										
0	1	2	3	4	5	6	7	8	9	10
11	12	13	14	15	16	17	18	19	20	

_____ − _____ = _____   _____ − _____ = _____

_____ − _____ = _____   _____ − _____ = _____

_____ − _____ = _____   _____ − _____ = _____

_____ − _____ = _____   _____ − _____ = _____

_____ − _____ = _____   _____ − _____ = _____

_____ − _____ = _____   _____ − _____ = _____

_____ − _____ = _____   _____ − _____ = _____

_____ − _____ = _____   _____ − _____ = _____

Activity 5 | Triplets

●●●

**Small Group
Activity**

**One (1) copy
per pair.
Also see
page 11.**

Description

Write differences for subtraction facts to make a game sheet. Play the game and be the first to capture three squares in a row.

Materials

Each pair of children needs

▶ Triplets game sheet, page 11

▶ Pencil, paper, and scissors

▶ 36 LinkerCubes®, 18 each of two colors

▶ A brown paper bag

Time

15 to 30 minutes

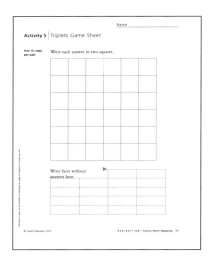

Getting Ready to Play

❶ Write 9 different subtraction facts on a piece of paper.

❷ Take turns. Write a fact, but not the answer, in a rectangle at the bottom of page 11.

❸ Write the answer for each fact in two different spaces on the game sheet.

❹ When all facts are written and game sheet spaces are filled, cut the facts apart. Put them in the paper bag. Put away the paper on which you wrote your facts.

Playing the Game

❶ Take turns playing.

❷ Draw a fact from the bag.

❸ Place your color LinkerCube® in a square with the answer to the fact you drew. Return the fact to the bag.

❹ The first player to get three LinkerCubes in a row wins the game.

© Creative Publications 32301

Activity 5 Triplets Game Sheet

One (1) copy per pair.

Write each answer in two squares.

Write facts without
answers here.

✂ - - - - - - - - - - - - - - - - -

Activity 6 | Partner Quizzes

● ● ●

Small Group Activity

One (1) copy per child. Also see page 13.

Description

Practice your facts with a friend. Seeing, hearing, saying, and then writing your facts really helps you remember them!

Materials

▶ Partner Quizzes, page 13, for each partner

▶ Pencil and paper and scissors

Time

15 to 20 minutes per day for four days

Day 1

1 Cut a piece of paper into 6 pieces. Write a different subtraction fact to practice on each piece of paper.

2 Read each fact out loud. Really think about what you are reading.

Day 2

1 Trade facts with your partner. Have your partner show you one of your facts and read the fact out loud to you.

2 Look at the fact and say it.

3 Turn this paper over and write the fact on the back.

4 Repeat for all 6 of your facts.

5 Trade jobs with your partner. Be sure to take back your facts when you finish.

6 Later, read each fact out loud. Really think about what you are reading.

© Creative Publications 32301

Activity 6 | Partner Quizzes

●●●
Small Group Activity

One (1) copy per child.

Day 3

1 Trade facts with your partner. Ask your partner to show you one of your facts. Read the fact out loud.

2 Have your partner hide the fact from you. Say the fact again.

3 Write the fact on a sheet of paper. Have your partner check the fact. Start over if you write the fact incorrectly.

4 Repeat for all 6 of your facts.

5 Trade jobs with your partner. Take your facts back when you finish.

6 Later, read each fact out loud. Really think about what you are reading.

Day 4

1 Give your facts to your partner.

2 Have your partner read a fact, but not the answer, to you.

3 Repeat the fact and give the answer. Write the fact on another piece of paper.

4 Have your partner check what you wrote. If it is not correct, have your partner show you the fact. Cross out what you wrote and go on to the next fact. Place the missed fact at the bottom of the pile to be read again.

5 Repeat for all 6 of your facts.

6 Trade jobs with your partner. Take your facts back when you finish.

7 Later in the day read each fact out loud.

Activity 7 | SubtractionCode

●●●
Small Group Activity

One (1) copy plus one (1) copy of page 15 per child.

Description
Choose facts for your partner to put into code. Then, try to break the code.

Materials
▶ Subtraction Code, page 15, for each pair

▶ Paper and pencil

Time
15 to 30 minutes

Directions

1 Write 8 subtraction facts on a piece of paper. Give the paper to your partner.

2 Cut the Subtraction Code sheet in half. Take one half and give the other half to your partner.

3 Use the code on your half of the code sheet to translate your partner's facts. Write each coded fact at the bottom of your partner's fact paper. Be sure to mix up the order.

4 Exchange papers. Try to match each coded fact with a fact you wrote.

5 If you need help, ask your partner for hints from his or her Code Clues.

Kaitlin

$2 - 1 = 1$ $10 - 1 = 9$
$5 - 2 = 3$ $7 - 5 = 2$
$9 - 8 = 1$ $7 - 3 = 4$
$6 - 5 = 1$ $6 - 4 = 2$

$\triangle - \wedge = \triangle$ $\triangle / - \triangle = \wedge$

© Creative Publications 32301

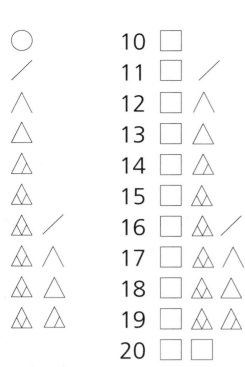

Code Clues

If your partner needs help, give these clues, one at a time.

Clue 1. Choose one of the facts that you put into code and tell your partner the fact.

Clue 2. $10 - \triangle = \triangle$

Clue 3. $\triangle / - / = 5$

Clue 4. $/ + / + / + / + / = \triangle$

Clue 5. Show the codes for each number, 1 through 5.

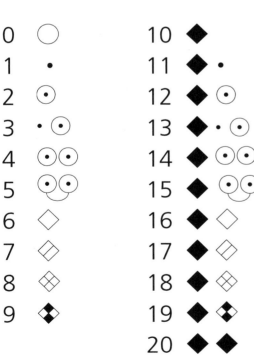

Code Clues

If your partner needs help, give these clues, one at a time.

Clue 1. Choose one of the facts that you put into code and tell your partner the fact.

Clue 2. $10 - \odot\!\odot = \odot\!\odot$

Clue 3. $\diamond - \bullet = 5$

Clue 4. $\bullet + \bullet + \bullet + \bullet + \bullet = \odot\!\odot$

Clue 5. Show the codes for each number, 1 through 5.

Activity 8 | Knock-Knock Joke Teller

Individual Practice Activity

One (1) copy plus one (1) copy of page 17 per child.

Description

Practice your subtraction facts with a knock-knock joke teller.

Materials

▶ One (1) copy of Knock-knock Joke Teller, page 17

▶ Scissors and pencil

Time

15 minutes

Directions

1 Write 12 subtraction facts on a piece of paper.

2 Cut out the joke teller on page 17. Fold according to directions.

3 Open the joke teller. Write one fact, but not the answer, in each box.

4 Refold. Your joke teller is ready to use.

Using the Joke Teller

1 Have your partner pick a fact.

2 Say the fact and give the answer. The answer will be the number of times to open and close the joke teller.

3 Have your partner choose another fact from the open joke teller. Work the joke teller again.

4 Have your partner pick a word instead of a fact. For example, if your partner picks "ya,"

You	Knock-knock
Partner	Who's there?
You	Ya
Partner	Ya who?

Answer with the word under the flap picked.

© Creative Publications 32301

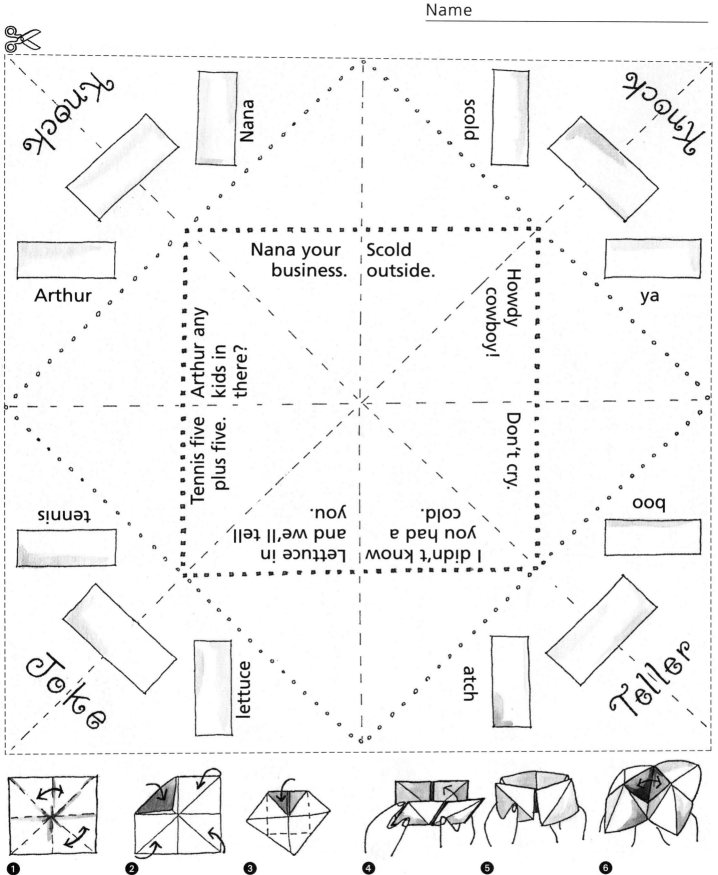

Knock

Nana

scold

Knock

Nana your business.

Scold outside.

Howdy cowboy!

Arthur

Arthur any kids in there?

ya

Tennis five plus five.

Don't cry.

tennis

Lettuce in and we'll tell you.

I didn't know you had a cold.

boo

Joke

lettuce

atch

Teller

1 Fold horizontally, then unfold. Fold vertically, then unfold. Repeat for folding on diagonals.

2 Fold each corner toward the middle with the words showing.

3 Turn paper over. Fold each corner toward the middle.

4 Fold in half, then unfold. Fold in half going the other direction, then unfold.

5 Put your thumbs and pointer fingers under the flaps of the underside.

6 Move fingers back and forth to open and close the joke teller.

Activity 9 | Subtraction Hopscotch

Individual Practice Activity

One (1) copy per child.

Description

This game of hopscotch will help you remember your facts. Play alone or with friends.

Materials

Sidewalk chalk and a marker

Time

15 minutes

Directions

1 Write 8 facts on the back of this paper.

2 On the sidewalk, make a hopscotch path that looks like this:

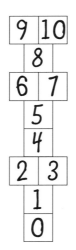

3 Toss your marker to land in the square that has the answer for your first fact.

4 If your marker lands in the right space, hop just as you would for a regular hopscotch game. Say the fact and answer as you hop.

5 If your marker does not land in the right space, use the number in the space where your marker landed and say a fact with that number as the answer. Hop to the space saying the fact and answer as you hop.

6 Toss your marker again to land in the square that has the answer for your fact.

7 Try to get through all your facts making as few tosses as you can. Eight is the best possible score!

© Creative Publications 32301

Activity 10 | Subject Subtraction

● Individual Practice Activity

One (1) copy per child.

Description

Write about the facts. The more you write, the easier it will be to remember those facts.

Materials

Paper, pencil, and crayons

Time

5 to 10 minutes per fact

---

idea box Think about how you use the fact in your life. If you buy a nickel candy with a dime, you get a nickel in change. $10 - 5 = 5$.

Draw a picture that illustrates your fact.

Try to create a rhyme or poem about the fact.

Directions

❶ Write a subtraction fact you want to memorize on each line.

_____

_____

_____

_____

❷ Choose one fact. Use it as a title on your blank paper. Think of ways to describe the fact. Look in the Idea Box for some ideas.

❸ Write as many descriptions of the fact as you can.

❹ Repeat this for each of your four subtraction facts.

$16 - 7 = 9$

I can remember it just fine because $17-7 = 10$
And if you take 1 from the 17 then you get 9.

□ □ □ □ □ □ □ □ □ ⊠
⊠ ⊠ ⊠ ⊠ ⊠ ⊠ ⊠

Activity 11 | Work Those Facts

Individual Practice Activity

One (1) copy per child.

Description

Practice your facts while you work out. Be subtraction fact fit!

Materials

▶ Pencil and paper

Time

10 minutes

Exercise Routine

Say each fact 4 times as you do each exercise.

Fact 1 Do jumping jacks.
Fact 2 Go up on tiptoes and back down.
Fact 3 Run in place.
Fact 4 Do deep knee bends.

Directions

1 Write 4 subtraction facts.

2 Put your facts in an order that is easy for you to remember.

3 Use the exercise routine here, or make up your own. Say a fact while you do the first exercise. When you change to the next fact, change to the next exercise in the routine.

4 Repeat your exercise routine over and over as you repeat your facts. Do this for ten minutes.

© Creative Publications 32301

Activity 12 | Mirror, Mirror

Individual
Practice
Activity

One (1) copy
per child.

Description

When you see your facts every day they become easier to remember.

Materials

▶ Pencil and paper

▶ Tape

Time

10 minutes per day for a week

Directions

❶ Choose four subtraction facts to practice. Write each fact and difference on a piece of paper.

❷ Fold the paper in half with the facts inside. On the outside, write the same facts but do not write the differences.

❸ Tape the paper to a mirror you look into several times a day. Tape the paper so it can be opened easily.

❹ Look at the paper and say each fact and its difference every time you are near the mirror. Check to be sure that you are correct by opening the paper.

Activity 13 | Fact-Slip Subtraction

● Individual Practice Activity

One (1) copy per child. Also see page 23.

Description

Use a fact slip to practice your subtraction facts.

Materials

▶ Fact-Slip Subtraction, page 23

▶ A pencil, a pair of scissors, and a book

Time

5 minutes each day for a week

Directions

❶ Write 8 subtraction facts to practice under "Facts" on the fact slip.

❷ Write the difference for that fact under "Differences."

❸ Cut out the fact slip and fold it so that the writing is showing.

❹ Place the fact slip in a book so only the first fact shows. Say the fact including the answer.

❺ Flip the book and check to make sure you said the fact correctly.

❻ Flip the book back over to the fact side. Pull the slip up so you can see the next fact.

❼ Repeat until you have completed all your facts.

© Creative Publications 32301

Activity 13 | Fact-Slip Subtraction

✂

Individual
Practice
Activity

One (1) copy
per child.

Fact Slip Facts	Differences
−	≈
−	≈
−	≈
−	≈
−	≈
−	≈
−	≈
−	≈

Fold

Bibliography

Practice Your Facts. Chicago, Creative Publications, Inc., 1999. These 80-page practice books offer traditional practice on all facts. Levels 1–5.

Holden, Linda, and Micaelia Randolph Brummett. *Understanding Addition & Subtraction.* Chicago, Creative Publications, Inc., 1988. Forty-eight carefully sequenced, reproducible lessons help children make connections between concrete experiences, pictorial representations, and abstract equations. The 128-page binder includes activities using linking cubes and counting chips.

Irvine, Rhea, and Kathryn Walker. *Smart Arithmetic, Grades 1-3.* Chicago, Creative Publications, Inc., 1995. The 96-page teacher resource book helps you guide your children in a thinking approach to computation as they invent their own algorithms. A start-up bank of suggested activities provides experiences in discourse, visual thinking, mental computation, and fact recall.

Leutzinger, Larry. *Facts that Last.* Chicago, Creative Publications, Inc., 1999. Four entire books devoted to fact strategies! Hands-on activities introduce children to each strategy, and follow-up practice ensures that they can use the strategy. There is a book for each operation.

National Council of Teachers of Mathematics. *Standards 2000.* Reston, Virginia, 2000. This document emphasizes the importance of mastering basic facts. Indeed, fast and accurate recall of basic facts is an essential tool in the mathematical toolkit.

Ward, Sandra. *Constructing Ideas About Number Combinations.* Chicago, Creative Publications, Inc., 1995. Fourteen one- to five-day explorations help children construct and deepen their understanding of addition and subtraction. Each exploration is clearly presented in an easy to use format and includes reproducible homework.

© Creative Publications 32301